CONTENTS

SETTING THE SCENE 4
• *Italy in the 15th century*

A YOUNG ARTIST 6
• *Growing up in the country* • *Moving to Florence with his family*
• *Joining Verrocchio's workshop* • *Master craftsman*

A MAN OF MANY TALENTS 16
• *Painter, sculptor, architect and engineer*
• *Moving to Milan and working for Duke Sforza*
• *Painting, sculpting, designing weapons and other war instruments*
• *Becoming famous*

SCIENTIST AND MATHEMATICIAN 24
• *Studying the human body* • *The Vitruvian Man* • *The Last Supper*

WAR AND WATER 28
• *Working in Venice* • *Designing fortresses, dams and flying machines*

MAPS AND THE MONA LISA 34
• *Making some of the earliest maps*
• *Painting The Mona Lisa, the most famous picture in the world*
• *Working in Florence and Milan* • *Leonardo's father dies*

ROME AND FRANCE 40
• *Working for the Pope in Rome*
• *Rivalry between Leonardo, Michelangelo and Raphael*
• *Being suspected of sorcery* • *Working for the king of France*

TIMELINE/DID YOU KNOW? 44

GLOSSARY 46

INDEX 48

Leonardo da Vinci was born to a young unmarried couple and both his parents soon married other people. Leonardo grew up to become a great genius. He was a painter, astronomer, sculptor, geologist, mathematician, botanist, animal behaviourist, inventor, engineer, architect and even a musician. Throughout his long career, Leonardo worked for kings, popes and dukes. He travelled and worked in Florence, Milan, Mantua, Rome, Venice, Pavia, Bologna and France. Not only did he paint pictures like The Mona Lisa, he also invented designs for a helicopter, a mechanical loom, a car, a bike and a multi-barrelled gun! One of his biggest problems was that he was ahead of his time and many of his inventions could not be made with the limited resources available during his lifetime.

DUCHY
OF
SAVOY

FRANCE

Florence, one of the cultural capitals of Italy in the 15th century

Italy in the 15th century was not the united country we know today. At that time, it was divided into many small independent states. The states were ruled by different leaders and even fought wars against each other to increase their power.

A - March of Montferrat

B - County of Asti

C - Republic of Lucca

D - Duchy of Modena

E - Duchy of Mantua

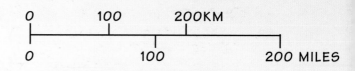

The Story of...

LEONARDO DA VINCI

Author
SUSIE HODGE

Leonardo da Vinci: *was the illegitimate son of a wealthy young man and a peasant girl. He was born on 15 April, 1452, in Vinci, Italy. He grew up to be a great inventor, scientist, military engineer, philosopher, botanist and mathematician, as well as a brilliant painter and sculptor. Many of his inventions were ahead of his time by centuries. From his simple beginnings, Leonardo went on to live and work at the courts of kings and dukes and was accepted, then as now, as a genius and 'Renaissance man'. He died in France on 2 May, 1519, at the age of 68.*

Andrea del Verrocchio: *born in Florence, Italy, in 1435, the son of a brickmaker, he was originally called Andrea di Michele di Francesco Cione. He became an extremely successful sculptor and painter and taught some of the greatest artists of the Renaissance. He died in Venice in 1488, when he was 53.*

Michelangelo: *was a sculptor, painter, architect and poet and, although 23 years younger, was Leonardo's greatest rival. He was born Michelangelo Buonarroti in Caprese, Italy, on 6 March, 1475. He became famous and was considered a genius even during his lifetime. He produced some of the greatest art ever made. He died in Rome on 18 February, 1564, when he was 89 years old.*

Raphael: *was younger than both Leonardo and Michelangelo, born on Good Friday, 6 April, 1483, in Urbino, Italy. His name was Raffaello Sanzio and his father was also a painter and poet. By the age of 17, he was classed as a 'master'. He admired Leonardo and Michelangelo, but they resented him. He died on his 37th birthday, Sunday, 6 April, 1520.*

Duke Ludovico Sforza: *born on 27 July, 1452, he was the Duke of Milan for only five years, from 1494 to 1500, but he ruled the city in his nephew's name for longer. After defeating the French, he was later defeated by them and died on 27 May, 1507, a prisoner in the castle of Loches, France. His castle, Castello Sforzesco, still stands in Milan.*

Pope Leo X: *was born Giovanni di Lorenzo de'Medici on 11 December, 1475, in Florence, Italy. His family was the most powerful in Florence at the time and he was Pope from 1513 to his death, eight years later. He tried to stop the Protestants from rising up. Leo X died on 1 December, 1521, in Rome.*

Copyright © ticktock Entertainment Ltd. 2006
First published in Great Britain in 2006 by ticktock Media Ltd.,
Unit 2, Orchard Business Centre, North Farm Road, Tunbridge Wells, Kent, TN2 3XF
ISBN 1 84696 043 6
Printed in China
A CIP catalogue record for this book is available from the British Library.

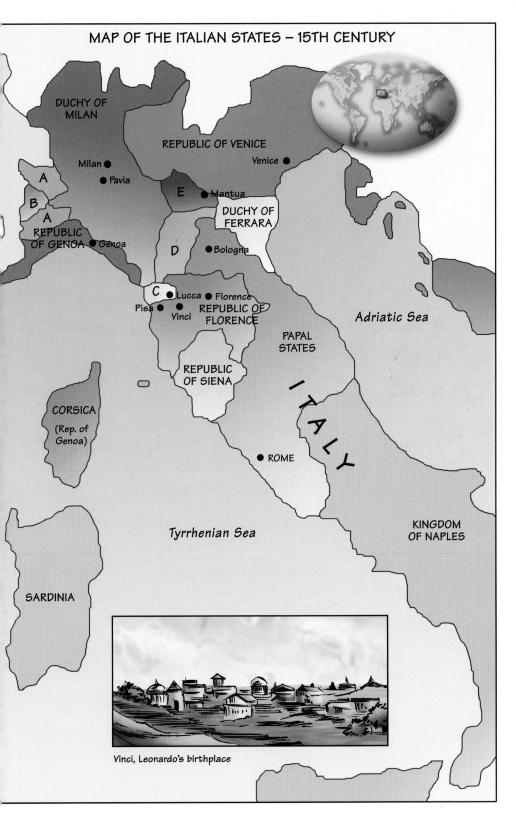

DUCHY OF MILAN

REPUBLIC OF VENICE

Milan ●

Venice ●

● Pavia

E

● Mantua

A

B

A

DUCHY OF FERRARA

REPUBLIC OF GENOA

● Genoa

D

● Bologna

C

● Lucca

● Florence

Pisa ●

Vinci

REPUBLIC OF FLORENCE

Adriatic Sea

PAPAL STATES

ITALY

REPUBLIC OF SIENA

Adriatic Sea

CORSICA

(Rep. of Genoa)

● ROME

Tyrrhenian Sea

KINGDOM OF NAPLES

SARDINIA

Vinci, Leonardo's birthplace

A YOUNG ARTIST

Leonardo was born near Vinci, in the countryside of Tuscany, Italy, on a spring evening in 1452. His mother, Caterina, was a young peasant woman. His father, Ser Piero, was from a fairly wealthy family. They did not marry, but they were both proud of their baby. Caterina kept Leonardo with her while he was a baby and Ser Piero visited them.

That's the city of Florence. We have a house there too my son. Soon, we'll move there as it is where your stepmother comes from.

When Leonardo was two years old, his father took him to live in his family's country house. There, Leonardo became close to his grandfather and his uncle. Leonardo's father, Ser Piero, soon married a young woman from another wealthy family.

Leonardo loved his father's brother, Francesco, and followed him around, always asking questions. Francesco loved Leonardo and told him all he knew.

You need to understand the countryside, Leonardo; then you can help me in the fields!

Yes, with the olives, grapes and wheat, Uncle Francesco!

As Leonardo grew up, he was very bright.

Look, Father, here are my ideas!

You are very clever, my boy. Although you cannot follow me in my work because you are illegitimate, I will see that you have the best teachers in Florence.

FAST FACT The Renaissance was a period when European scholars and artists were inspired with new ideas after the rediscovery of ancient Greece and Rome.

Florence was an exciting place to be. New and innovative building work was taking place, and most of the best artists in Europe worked there.

Verrocchio, what do you think of my son's artistic abilities?

I've never seen such talent in an untrained boy. One day, he will be a greater artist than I. He can certainly come and learn with me.

When Leonardo was 14, Ser Piero took him to the workshop (or bottega) of the famous artist, Andrea del Verrocchio.

Leonardo began working as an apprentice to Verrocchio in Florence.

The workshop received orders for paintings, sculpture, ornaments, armour, jewellery and many other things.

Leonardo learned how to draw, paint, cast bronze, make jewellery, play music and much more.

In the 15th century, Florence was particularly lively. Scholars, philosophers and artists came to discuss their ideas. There were workshops of all kinds and people played music and strolled through the streets, meeting and talking.

Keep still, Leonardo! I've nearly finished.

They're making me laugh.

Any requests?

Yes, play that one again, and shut up so we can sing the chorus this time.

Sometimes Leonardo was Verrocchio's model.

Leonardo learned to play the lute and to sing.

Often, other artists would come to the workshop to discuss ideas with Verrocchio and his apprentices.

When Verrocchio had a large piece of work to produce, all the apprentices worked on it.

FAST FACT From medieval times, people in various trades grouped together in associations or guilds. These groups decided on rules for their trades and set prices for their services.

Leonardo often found teachers of science, mathematics and philosophy to question.

How does illness enter our bodies?

So many questions! We don't have all the answers, but perhaps one day, you will find out.

One day, Leonardo and two of the other apprentices, Botticelli and Credi, were helping Verrocchio with his painting of "The Baptism of Christ".

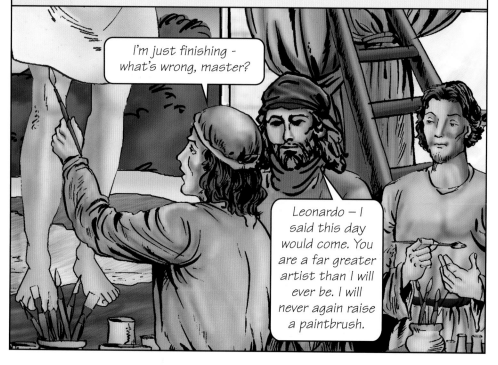

I'm just finishing - what's wrong, master?

Leonardo – I said this day would come. You are a far greater artist than I will ever be. I will never again raise a paintbrush.

It was stimulating to be in Florence at that time. Wealthy merchants and bankers paid for architects to build innovative new buildings. With his thirst for knowledge, it was the perfect place for Leonardo da Vinci to be.

In 1472, he became a master craftsman of his trade and had earned the right to be called 'master'.

Now patrons will pay him to work for them!

Look at my son, Francesco! The most famous guild for artists, the Compagna di San Luca has made him a member!

In 1476, now officially a master, Leonardo opened his own workshop. Leonardo continued to work as an apprentice with Verrocchio until 1477. His paintings, sculptures and metalwork astonished people – they had never seen such realistic work. In his spare time, he drew and painted whatever and whenever he could, producing the kind of art that no one had seen before.

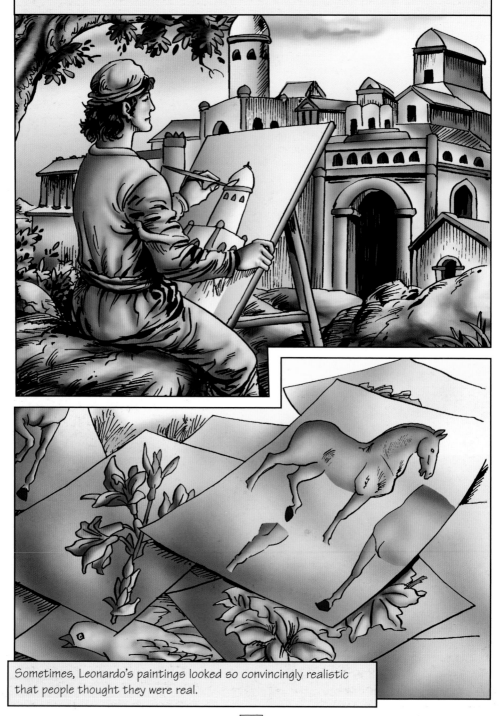

Sometimes, Leonardo's paintings looked so convincingly realistic that people thought they were real.

When Leonardo worked in his own workshop, he had his own apprentices to help him and to learn from him.

Mix up some more of that red paint, please!

At last, my reputation is growing. Once the Medicis pay me, everyone will want my work!

So young man, we have seen your work and we want you to work for us.

The powerful Medici family asked him to their magnificent home.

FAST FACT The Medici family was made up of powerful, wealthy and feared merchants and bankers. They ruled Florence between 1434 and 1737. They encouraged art, building, music and scholarship.

A MAN OF MANY TALENTS

Although Leonardo was running a successful workshop in Florence, He went to Milan in 1482, to meet the powerful Ludovico Sforza.

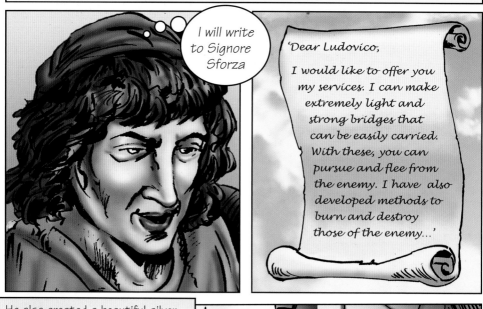

I will write to Signore Sforza

'Dear Ludovico,

I would like to offer you my services. I can make extremely light and strong bridges that can be easily carried. With these, you can pursue and flee from the enemy. I have also developed methods to burn and destroy those of the enemy...'

He also created a beautiful silver lute to impress his wealthy patron.

As the weeks and months passed, Leonardo worked on many things for Ludovico (who had now become a duke), from weapons to buildings, to bridges and more.

He designed an armoured tank...

and a multi-barrelled machine gun.

Leonardo developed techniques to create shadows in his paintings.

Leonardo found a place to live with the Predis brothers who were also artists.

Thank you for the bread and wine, friends.

You make it look so easy. I have never seen the Virgin and Son look so real!

Make sure you've put a bloom in the skin like I showed you.

Even while he was working for Duke Ludovico, Leonardo didn't stop investigating and inventing. Although he hated war, he was being paid to design new and dangerous weapons.

He designed this giant crossbow fixed to wagon wheels.

The narrow streets of Milan are dirty. Too many are dying of plague. This is my design for an ideal city that will banish dirt and disease.

The truth about the world can only be learned through studying everything closely and thinking about it. Many of Leonardo's sketches show this.

Leonardo was fascinated by beauty, but he also drew many funny and grotesque caricatures

Leonardo opened another workshop in Milan, called "The Accademia Leonardi Vinci".

Leonardo was so busy that he took on five apprentices. He loved to tell jokes and stories to people who visited his studio.

Your studio, Leonardo, is always crowded with people, singing, painting and talking.

Yes! Everyone wants to be friends with the great Leonardo da Vinci.

FAST FACT During the Renaissance, artists worked out a way of making flat paintings look three-dimensional. Leonardo used this technique in his paintings, drawings and designs. It was called linear perspective.

But before Leonardo could complete his amazing statue, French troops marched into Italy. The invasion put an end to the plans for the grand project.

The bronze was eventually used to make cannons, and later the French troops destroyed Leonardo's clay model of the horse for target practice.

SCIENTIST AND MATHEMATICIAN

Leonardo's curiosity was never-ending. He even cut up dead bodies from a local hospital. This was a crime punishable by death, so he took a great risk.

Through his studies, he worked out all sorts of things about the body that had not been understood before.

He watched operations. It was the first time in history that the body became an object of scientific research.

With the help of someone who worked in the hospital, Leonardo took corpses of poor people to cut up in his studio.

Leonardo was kept busy with many projects for Ludovico. One was the "Feast of Paradise", in honour of the marriage of Ludovico's nephew to the granddaughter of the King of Naples.

FAST FACT Doctors were only just starting to realise that the best way to learn about how the body works was to look inside.

Leonardo made friends with the mathematician, Luca Pacioli, a Franciscan friar. Pacioli taught Leonardo a lot about mathematics and in return, Leonardo illustrated Pacioli's book about proportion.

My drawing, The Vitruvian Man, is based on the work of the ancient Roman architect Vitruvius. It shows the proportions of the human body perfectly

In 1495, Leonardo was asked to paint a huge mural of Jesus and the disciples at The Last Supper for the dining hall of a monastery in Milan.

I've invented a new technique so I can brush paint directly on to a wall. It makes the colours luminous. I'm using mathematics to compose this ten-metre long picture and I've broken with tradition by putting the traitor Judas in with all the other disciples. It's a lively picture, but the monks who are paying for it are cross because I'm taking so long.

In 1499, when the French took control of Milan, Leonardo left with Pacioli, Salaì and his other apprentices. Times were changing for the great artist.

At first, Leonardo, Pacioli, Salaí and the apprentices went to Mantua in Italy. Then they travelled to Venice.

Ah, Venice, the enemy of Milan, but such a powerful place! I'm sure to find success here.

The motion of flight fascinated Leonardo. He researched how birds' wings are constructed and how they glide and land. With the help of this research he invented a flying machine. His other designs included a fortress and a diving suit.

Flying fascinates me. How are bird's wings constructed? How do they glide and land? I can work it out and make this machine fly!

This fortress will keep everyone safe inside and no enemy could penetrate its walls.

Leonardo's talents impressed the people of Venice and he quickly managed to find work helping the war effort against the Ottoman Empire.

Leonardo, we invite you to stay in Venice and work for us as a military engineer.

Thank you, I will be happy to stay.

Venice was under threat from the Ottoman Empire. When Leonardo moved there, Ottoman warships lay off the coast, waiting to invade.

FAST FACT The Ottoman Empire was based in present day Turkey. Ottoman sultans (leaders) had captured many Christian lands, and now they were after Venice!

Leonardo worked on many plans to stop an Ottoman invasion.

With this wooden dam, we can flood the Ottomans. Then they'll either drown or flee and never return.

Leonardo then went on to design a submarine, a deep-sea diving suit and breathing apparatus to allow soldiers to walk on the seabed.

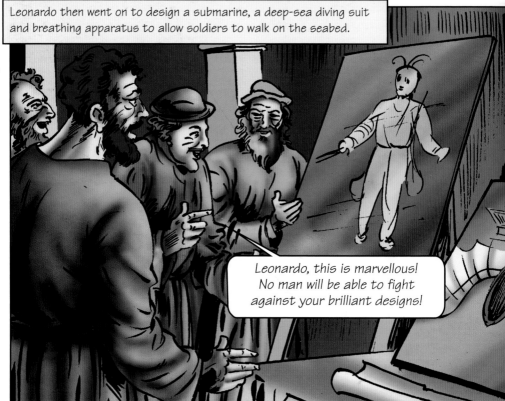

Leonardo, this is marvellous! No man will be able to fight against your brilliant designs!

After some months, Leonardo and his friends returned to Florence. He spent some time with his father, who was now married to his fourth wife and had eleven other children.

The people of Florence were pleased to have Leonardo back. In 1502, the cunning and feared military ruler, Cesare Borgia, came to see him.

Leonardo travelled with Cesare throughout Italy, studying cities and fortresses and organising building work.

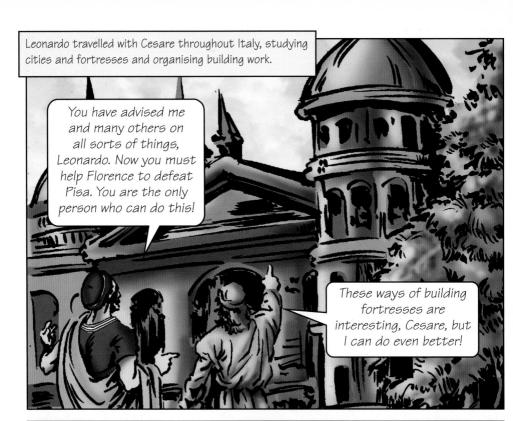

Leonardo met Niccolò Machiavelli, second chancellor to Florence. They respected each other's intelligence and became friends. They worked together on some of Leonardo's inventions and ideas.

It is good to meet you Leonardo.

I am honoured to meet the esteemed writer and philosopher Niccolò Machiavelli..

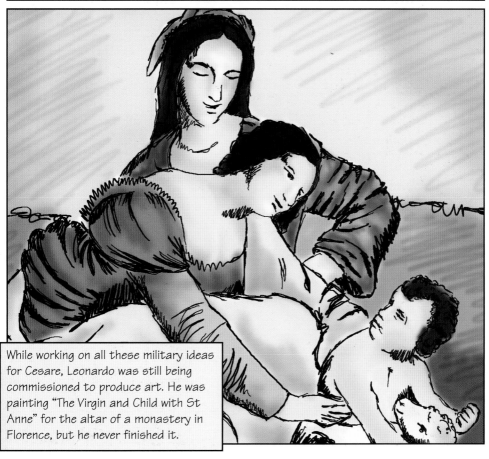

While working on all these military ideas for Cesare, Leonardo was still being commissioned to produce art. He was painting "The Virgin and Child with St Anne" for the altar of a monastery in Florence, but he never finished it.

MAPS AND THE MONA LISA

Using a magnetic compass and his knowledge of mathematics, Leonardo made accurate maps of many places. He was one of the first people to do this.

Leonardo was famous for painting marvellous portraits for many wealthy people in Florence.

Michelangelo, his greatest rival, was working on a battle scene in the same place as Leonardo was working. The two artists and their apprentices kept out of each other's way.

Around 1503, Leonardo was asked to paint a portrait of a young woman, called Lisa, by her husband.

Pacioli, this is going to be one of my best ever!

Fantastic!

The printing press had recently been invented, and now books could be printed and bought fairly easily. Now Leonardo could read lots of books and could also play from sheet music.

Great invention, but I could improve the printing press.

Hey Leonardo, why the fascination with nature?

No point trying to understand Leonardo! He's cleverer than all of us put together!

I want to discover the secrets behind everything!

Michelangelo, Raphael and Leonardo admired each other's work, but were jealous of each other.

Ha, those two can't copy this! I've captured her emotions and her mind!

I want to know how he made her face so mysterious.

She looks so real! How did he keep her smiling while he was painting this?

In 1504, Leonardo's father died, leaving everything to his legitimate sons, not Leonardo.

This is the last will and testament of Ser Piero da Vinci...

However, Leonardo's Uncle Francesco left his land to his favourite nephew. Leonardo's nine half-brothers tried to change their Uncle Francesco's will, but they could not.

I'll never forget you, Uncle Francesco.

Leonardo, I'm dying, but I've left you my land. Your father left all to your half-brothers and sisters, but you have always been my special nephew.

In 1507, Leonardo became court painter to Louis XII of France who was living in Milan.

Don't you feel bad siding with the French – the enemies of Ludovico?

I side with no one, Salaí! Louis appreciates my work, pays me good money and has given me this beautiful studio.

ROME AND FRANCE

In 1512, Ludovico's son drove the French out of Milan, so once more Leonardo had no patron. The Medici family no longer ruled Florence, but were powerful in Rome. So in 1513, Leonardo went to Rome.

Pope Leo X was a Medici.

All Leonardo's ideas seemed to be ahead of their time.

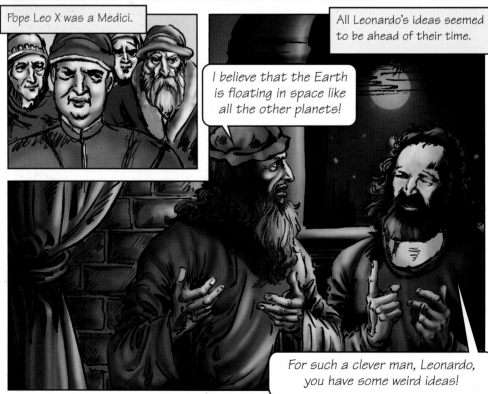

Michelangelo and Raphael (who were both much younger artists) had been working in Rome for the previous Pope, and now for Pope Leo X. They were producing amazing works of art. Leonardo was now employed by Pope Leo X, too.

Meanwhile, Leonardo still studied bodies closely to find out how everything works.

Their work is wonderful, but they have learned a lot from me!

Then Pope Leo X asked Leonardo to produce a religious painting.

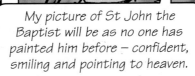

My picture of St John the Baptist will be as no one has painted him before – confident, smiling and pointing to heaven.

Leonardo was still taking risks by cutting up corpses. One day, his actions were discovered and he was accused of sorcery.

Run, Melzi! Run Salaí! The Pope's guards will kill me if they catch me.

Leonardo met the king of France, Francois I, during this time. The two men admired each other. So Leonardo travelled to the French court.

This is of a young woman from Florence.

I would like to buy some of your work, Leonardo. Please stay here in France; you will be my most honoured guest.

So in 1516, Leonardo accepted the French king's invitation to become his chief painter, architect and mechanic at Amboise in France. By then, Leonardo was 64.

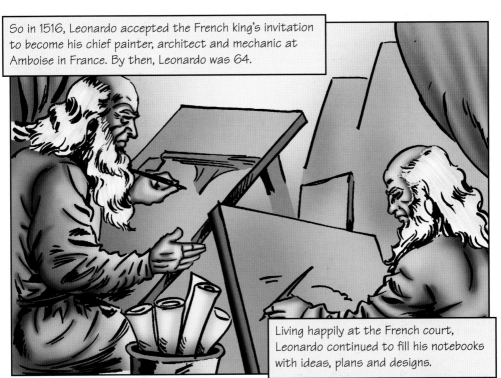

Living happily at the French court, Leonardo continued to fill his notebooks with ideas, plans and designs.

Leonardo had written a will, leaving money and land to Salaí, his half-brothers and his servants and all his books, writings and paintings to Melzi. On 2 May, 1519, he died in the arms of his good friend, King Francois of France.

Leonardo, what will your friends and the world do without you?

I am dying Francois. Thank you for being such a good friend to me.

Leonardo da Vinci is one of the most famous artists of all time as well as a genius who explored many things. He lived during a time of discovery, power and intrigue and many of his ideas anticipated later discoveries in anatomy, aeronautics and more.

1452: *Leonardo is born in Anchiano, near Vinci, Italy, to Piero and Caterina.*

1466: *Leonardo moves to Florence and enters Verrocchio's workshop.*

1472: *Leonardo joins the artists' guild, the Compagna di San Luca.*

1475: *Michelangelo born.*

1476: *Leonardo sets up his own workshop. He begins writing notebooks of ideas and works for the Medici family.*

1482: *Leonardo moves to Milan. He works for Ludovico Sforza as engineer, architect, painter and sculptor.*

1483: *Raphael born. Leonardo begins work on "The Virgin of the Rocks".*

1489: *Leonardo begins work on a colossal horse statue for Duke Ludovico Sforza.*

1490: *Leonardo designs scenery and costumes for the Feast of Paradise on 13th January. He draws "The Vitruvian Man" and paints "The Lady with the Ermine".*

1495: *Leonardo begins "The Last Supper" in the refectory of the monastery of Santa Maria delle Grazie in Milan.*

1498: *Leonardo completes "The Last Supper" and ceiling paintings at Sforzesco Castle in Milan.*

1499: *The French invade Milan and destroy the clay model of Leonardo's giant horse statue. In December, Leonardo travels to Mantua.*

1502: *Cesare Borgia hires Leonardo to work for him in Florence as senior military engineer and architect. Leonardo meets Niccolò Machiavelli.*

1503: *Leonardo makes plans to divert the River Arno during the siege of Pisa. Raphael arrives in Florence to study Leonardo's work. Rivalry begins between the three artists. Leonardo produces some of the first accurate maps to ever be made and starts painting "The Mona Lisa".*

1504: *Leonardo's father dies aged 80, leaving all his money to Leonardo's nine half-brothers and two half-sisters. Leonardo studies flight and designs a flying machine.*

1506: *Leonardo finishes "The Mona Lisa; he returns to Milan.*

1507: *Uncle Francesco dies, leaving Leonardo land. Leonardo becomes the 'King's Painter' to Louis XII, King of France.*

1508: *Leonardo completes a second version of "The Virgin of the Rocks". Michelangelo begins painting the ceiling of the Sistine Chapel in Rome.*

1513: *Leonardo moves to Rome and lives in the Vatican with the new Pope, Leo X.*

1515: *Leonardo paints St John the Baptist and makes a mechanical lion for the new French king, Francois I.*

1516: *Leonardo moves to Amboise in France, the court of Francois I.*

1519: *Leonardo dies in the company of Francois I, Melzi and Salaí.*

1. *If his parents had been married, Leonardo's name would have been Leonardo di Ser Piero da Vinci, meaning Leonardo, son of Ser Piero, from Vinci.*

2. *Leonardo ended up with 17 half brothers and sisters! His mother married and had five more children and his father eventually had twelve more.*

3. *"The Last Supper" is carefully proportioned and balanced to show its holiness. Leonardo learned this idea from the ancient Greeks and Romans.*

4. *Leonardo invented a way of painting "The Last Supper" to make the colours extra bright, but the paint began to deteriorate almost immediately.*

5. *In the 14th century, China stopped trading with the outside world, so rich merchants spent their money on Italian art rather than buying luxuries from the East.*

6. *Many of Leonardo's painted backgrounds include fantastic landscapes and buildings, seemingly seen through a veil of mist. This was a technique he invented, called sfumato, or 'smoky'.*

7. *As well as linear perspective, Leonardo also used 'atmospheric' or 'aerial perspective' to make his backgrounds appear to fade into the distance.*

8. *Throughout his lifetime Leonardo designed many buildings with great architectural skill and knowledge. Not one of his designs was constructed, but his ideas inspired many later architects.*

9. *Leonardo was an animal lover and a vegetarian. He drew all kinds of animals in his sketchbooks and had many pets.*

10. *Without any training, Leonardo effectively designed buildings with*  *military reinforcements, cannons, guns, ramps, tanks and other weapons.*

11. *Leonardo learned how a baby grows inside its mother, including the function of the umbilical cord, the womb and the liquid that surrounds and protects the growing baby.*

12. *Leonardo invented a kind of helicopter, which he called an 'airscrew'. He never constructed it, but his theory was right and modern helicopters are based on the same principle.*

13. *As well as flying machines and helicopters, Leonardo invented the first parachute!*

14. *Leonardo dreamed of machines made for transportation on water, in the air and across land. One of his inventions was a motor that is a forerunner of the modern car engine.*

GLOSSARY

Anatomy: *The study of bodies.*

Animal behaviourist: *A person who understands how and why animals behave as they do.*

Apprentice: *A young person who is taught by an expert. In the Renaissance, young boys who wanted to become artists trained as apprentices in the workshops of skilled artists.*

Architect: *Someone who designs and plans the construction of buildings.*

Aeronautics: *The design and construction of aircraft.*

Astronomer: *A person who studies the science of astronomy – the study of outer space.*

Atmospheric or aerial perspective: *A way of creating images that appear to have depth through the use of colour – the further away objects are, the bluer they become.*

Botanist: *A scientist who studies plants.*

Bottega: *A workshop or studio.*

Canal: *A manmade river used for travel and shipping.*

Commission: *Paying someone to do some work for you, or to make something for you.*

Contours: *Outlines.*

Corpses: *Dead bodies.*

Deteriorate *To fade or become weaker.*

Disciples: *People who learn from a teacher. In the New Testament, Jesus had twelve disciples.*

Divert: *Send in another direction or re-route.*

Engineer: *Someone who uses science and mathematics to solve practical problems and to make useful goods, such as machines.*

Fortress: *A stronghold or castle.*

Geologist: *A scientist who studies the origin, history and structure of the Earth.*

Fresco: *Italian word for fresh; in art it means the technique of applying wet paint to damp, freshly plastered walls so that the painting becomes part of the wall.*

Guild: *An association (or group) of people who share a trade or craft.*

Illegitimate: *Born to parents who are not married.*

Innovative: *Being original and inventive, and having unique ideas.*

Linear perspective: *A way of creating the appearance of depth – making a painting with a 2D surface appear 3D. It makes objects. appear smaller the further away they are.*

Loom: *A machine for weaving.*

Luminous: *Glowing with light.*

Lute: *A stringed musical instrument.*

Monastery: *Home for a community of monks.*

Multi-barrelled gun: *A powerful gun, similar to a machine gun that can fire lots of bullets or shot at once.*

Mural: *A wall painting.*

Patron: *A person (or group of people) who pays someone else to produce something that they want, such as a painting or sculpture.*

Perspective: *Making objects on a 2D surface look 3D, and giving the illusion of depth and distance.*

Philosopher: *A wise person who calmly analyses and thinks about life.*

Pigment: *Powdered colour which, when mixed with liquid, becomes paint.*

Pope: *The head of the Roman Catholic Church.*

Portrait: *Painting or drawing of a person.*

Redirect: *To send in another direction.*

Rediscovery: *To discover or find again.*

Renaissance: *During the 14th century, starting in Italy and spreading across Europe, there was a rebirth of learning and a great interest in creative arts and ideas. This period became known as the Renaissance, but not until the 19th century, 500 years after the Renaissance began.*

Scholars: *People who study and learn.*

Sfumato: *A technique of painting that Leonardo invented. It means smoky and describes his way of painting soft, blended areas on his paintings.*

Ser: *An Italian title similar to 'Sir' in English.*

Signore: *The Italian word for 'mister'.*

Tempera: *Powdered colour pigment mixed with egg.*

Vitruvian Man: *A man drawn by Leonardo, following the perfect proportions that the ancient Greek architect Vitruvius had worked out.*

Will: *A document that people write explaining how their money and belongings will be distributed after their deaths.*

Workshop: *A place where work is carried out. In the Renaissance, artists' workshops, or 'bottegas', were where patrons went to commission work and where artists produced their work, while training their apprentices.*

A
Accademia Leonardi Vinci 21
aerial perspective 45
anatomy 24, 25, 39
apprentices 46
    Leonardo's 15, 18, 21,
    Verrocchio's 9–12, 14
architects 13, 45, 46
armoured tanks 19
atmospheric perspective 45
B
babies 45
Baptism of Christ
    (Verrocchio) 12
the body 24–26, 41
Borgia, Cesare 31–33
bottegas 8, 46
Botticelli 12
bronze statue 22–23
C
canals 32, 46
caricatures 21
cars 45
Castello Sforzesco 17
casts 9
Caterina (mother) 6
commissions 22–23, 33, 46
corpses 24–25, 42, 46
Credi 12
crossbows 20
D
dams 30
diving suits 28, 30
doctors 25
E
engineers 29, 31, 46
F
Feast of Paradise 25
Florence 4–15, 31–34
flying machines 28, 39, 45

fortresses 17, 28, 32, 46
Francesco (uncle) 7, 38
Francois I 42–43
frescoes 46
G
guilds 11, 13, 46
H
helicopters 45
I
illegitimate birth 6–7, 46
innovation 8, 13, 46
Italy 4–5, 23
L
Last Supper 27, 45
Leonardo da Vinci 2
linear perspective 21, 45, 46
Louis XII 38–39
luminous effects 27
lutes 10, 16, 47
M
Machiavelli, Niccolò 33
maps 34
master craftsmen 13, 14
mathematics 12, 26–27, 34
Medici family 15
Melzi 39, 43
Michelangelo 2, 35, 37, 41
Milan 4–5, 16–22, 27, 38
Mona Lisa 35–37
monasteries 27, 33, 47
multi-barrelled guns 4, 19, 47
murals 47
O
oil paints 11
Ottoman Empire 29–30
P
Pacioli, Luca 26–28
parachutes 45
patrons 13, 31, 47
perspective 21, 45, 46, 47
philosophers 10, 12, 33, 47
Piero (father) 6–8, 31, 38
pigment 47

Pisa 32
Pope Leo X 2, 40–41
portraits 34–37, 47
Predis brothers 19, 39
printing press 37
proportion 26
R
Raphael 2, 37, 41
realistic art 14–15
Renaissance 4, 7, 21, 47
Rome 40–42
S
Salaì 18, 39, 43
scholars 7, 10, 47
science 12, 24–27
Sforza, Duke Ludovico
    2, 16–22, 25
sfumato technique 36, 45, 47
shadow techniques 19
statue commission 22–23
submarines 30
T
tempera 11, 47
V
Venice 4–5, 28–30
Verrocchio, Andrea del
    2, 8–12, 14
Vinci 5, 6
Virgin and Child with
    St Anne 33
Vitruvian man 26, 47
W
weapons 17–20, 45
wills 38, 43, 47
workshops 8–12, 14, 47